The Magic Flute

A Chinese legend adapted by Gill Munton

Series Editor: Louis Fidge

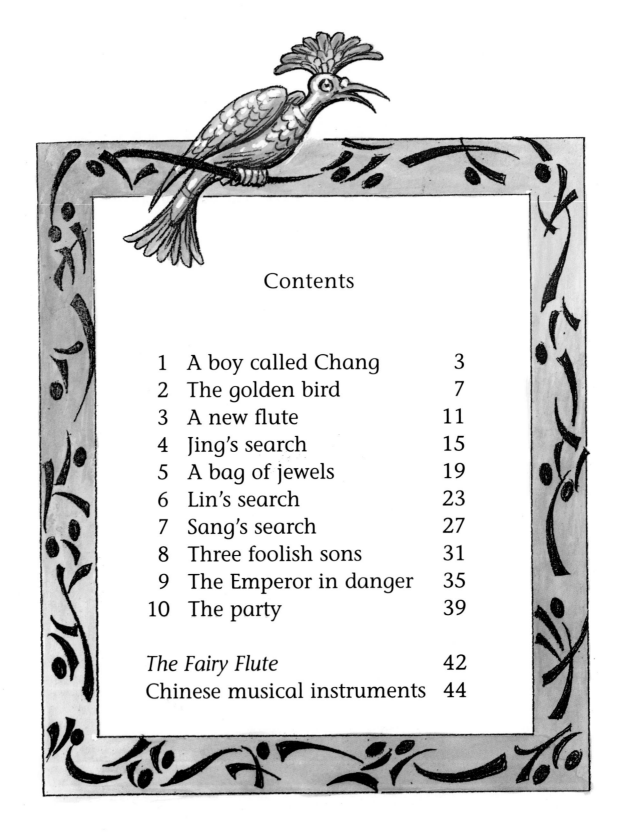

Contents

Chapter 1
A boy called Chang

'Chang! Come and play your flute for us!'
the people shouted.

Chang laughed, and picked up his flute.
He liked to look after the sheep,
but he **loved** to play his flute.

The people stopped and listened.
No one talked when Chang started to play.
When Chang played, it made them think happy thoughts.

Soon it was time for bed. Chang put down his flute.
Then he took the sheep to the field near his house
for the night.

The next morning, the Emperor came
to Chang's little house!

'Why is the Emperor here to see **me**?' Chang thought.

The Emperor took Chang to the field.

'How many sheep do you look after for me, Chang?'
he asked.

'Twenty, sir.'

'And how many sheep are in my field now?'
the Emperor asked.

'I don't know, sir,' Chang replied.

'Then I will tell you.
Nineteen!
Only nineteen, Chang!'

Chang counted. '… eighteen, nineteen!'
There were only nineteen sheep in the field.

'One of my sheep is lost!
Why is it lost?'
the Emperor asked.

'I don't know, sir,' Chang replied.

'Then I will tell you.
It is lost because you play your flute,
and you don't look after my sheep!'
the Emperor said angrily.

The Emperor took Chang back to his little house.

'Give me that flute!' he said.

'But, sir …'

'Give me the flute, Chang!'

The flute was under Chang's bed.
Chang picked it up, and gave it to the Emperor.
The Emperor broke the flute into two pieces.

'Now go!' the Emperor said. 'And don't come back!'

Chapter 2

The golden bird

There were only nineteen sheep
because the Emperor tricked Chang.
He took one sheep out of the field and hid it.

The Emperor tricked Chang
because he was jealous of him.

'The people love that boy more than they love me!'
he said. 'But now he has gone!
Now they will love me again!'

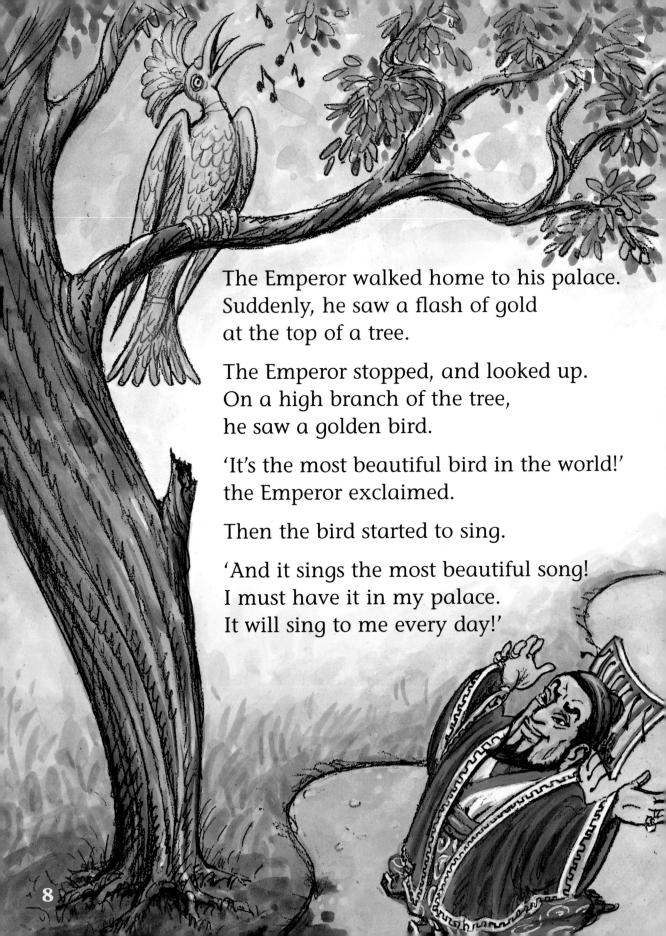

The Emperor walked home to his palace.
Suddenly, he saw a flash of gold
at the top of a tree.

The Emperor stopped, and looked up.
On a high branch of the tree,
he saw a golden bird.

'It's the most beautiful bird in the world!'
the Emperor exclaimed.

Then the bird started to sing.

'And it sings the most beautiful song!
I must have it in my palace.
It will sing to me every day!'

The Emperor had three sons.
The next day, he asked them all to come and see him.

'Yesterday I saw the most beautiful golden bird,' he said.
'And it sang the most beautiful song.
I want you to catch it for me.
If you catch it, you can have …
my silver sword!'

The Emperor's silver sword was beautiful
– and it was very valuable!

The Emperor's three sons were greedy.

Jing was the eldest son.
'I will go first,' said Jing.
'I will catch the golden bird,
and then Father's silver sword will be mine!'

His brothers laughed.

'You may be the eldest,
but you will not catch that bird, Jing.
And then it will be our turn to try!' they said.

Jing went to look for the golden bird.

Chapter 3

A new flute

Chang was sad as he walked away from his little house.
He loved the sheep, and he looked after them well.

Chang walked through a village,
and an old man called to him.

'What is wrong, my boy?
You look sad! Can I help you?'

'Yes, I **am** sad,' said Chang.
'I liked looking after the Emperor's sheep
and playing my flute.
But then the Emperor told me to go,
because I lost one of his sheep.
He broke my flute.
Now I have nowhere to go.'

'Come to my house,' the old man said.
He put his arm round the boy.
I will make you a new flute!'

The old man took a long piece of bamboo
and started to make a new flute.
Chang sat and watched him.

In the evening, the old man said,
'Here is your new flute, Chang.
Try it!'

Chang picked up the flute and started to play.

'Thank you!' he said.
'It sounds much better than my old one.
It sounds – like magic!'

That night, Chang played his magic flute.
Soon, people came to listen.

They stood in a circle around Chang and listened.
The animals wanted to hear the magic flute, too.

And at the top of a tree, a golden bird sat on a branch.
As Chang played his flute, the bird sang a beautiful song.

Chapter 4
Jing's search

'All day, Jing looked for the golden bird.

'It must be here somewhere,' he said. 'I **will** find it!'

He came to the village.
The old man was in his garden.
He was picking red cherries from a cherry tree.

'I will ask him about the bird,' thought Jing.

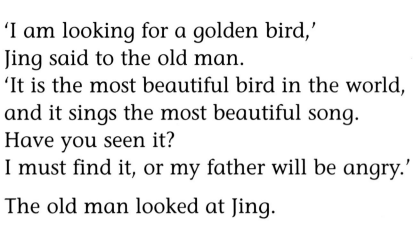

'I am looking for a golden bird,'
Jing said to the old man.
'It is the most beautiful bird in the world,
and it sings the most beautiful song.
Have you seen it?
I must find it, or my father will be angry.'

The old man looked at Jing.

'Oh?' he said. 'Is your father often angry?'

'My father is the Emperor,' said Jing.
'An Emperor can be angry whenever he likes!'

'I understand,' said the old man.
'Yes, I can help you to find the golden bird.
But you must pay me.'

'How much?' asked Jing.

'You must pay me a bag of jewels!
You must take a bag of jewels into the forest this evening.
You will hear the sound of a flute.
Follow the sound, and you will find the golden bird.'

'Thank you, sir,' said Jing. 'I will do as you say.'

As he walked back to the palace, he thought,
'Yes, I **will** pay a bag of jewels for the golden bird.
Then I can give the bird to my father,
and I will have his silver sword!'

Chapter 5
A bag of jewels

At the palace, Jing put some jewels in a bag.
That evening, he went into the forest.

Soon, Jing heard a sound.
It was the sound of a flute!

Jing followed the sound.

After a while, Jing saw a boy.

The boy was playing a bamboo flute.
People and animals sat in a circle around the boy.

Jing saw the golden bird sitting on a branch
at the top of a tree.

As the boy played the flute, the bird sang a beautiful song.

Jing walked up to the boy and held up the bag of jewels.

'An old man told me to come here,' he said.
'I will give you these jewels.
Will you give me that golden bird?'

The boy took the bag of jewels.
Then he played his flute.

At once, the bird flew down from the tree
and sat on the boy's shoulder.

He gently picked up the bird, and gave it to Jing.

Jing put the golden bird under his arm,
and set off back to the palace.

'That was easy!' he laughed.
'I will give the golden bird to my father –
and he will give me the silver sword!'

But then he heard the flute again.
The golden bird heard it, too.

In a flash of gold, it flew from under Jing's arm –
and flew away into the forest.

Chapter 6

Lin's search

The Emperor's second son was called Lin.
When Jing came back without the golden bird,
Lin said, 'Now it is my turn to try and catch the bird!'

Jing said, 'I **did** catch the bird! I put it under my arm!
But when it heard the boy playing the flute, it flew away!
I gave a bag of jewels to that boy!'

Lin thought, 'I will find the boy with the flute.
Then I will find the bird!
I will take a bag of jewels, too.'

The next day, Lin went into the forest.
Soon, he heard the sound of a flute!

A boy was playing a bamboo flute.
People and animals sat in a circle around the boy.
As the boy played the flute, the bird sand a beautiful song.

Lin walked up the boy and held up the bag of jewels.

He said, 'I will give you these jewels.
Will you give me that golden bird?'

The boy took the bag of jewels. Then he played his flute.

At once, the bird flew down from the tree
and sat on the boy's shoulder.

He picked up the bird gently, and gave it to Lin.

Lin put the golden bird in his basket,
and set off back to the palace.

'That was easy!' he laughed.
'I will give the golden bird to my father –
and he will give me the silver sword!'

But then he heard the flute again.
The golden bird heard it, too.
In a flash of gold, it flew from Lin's basket –
and flew away into the forest.

Chapter 7
Sang's search

The Emperor's youngest son was called Sang.
When Lin came back without the golden bird,
Sang said, 'Now it is my turn to try and catch the bird!'

Lin said, 'I **did** catch the bird! I put it in my basket!
But when it heard the boy playing the flute, it flew away!
I gave a bag of jewels to that boy!'

Sang thought, 'I will find the boy with the flute,
Then I will find the bird!
I will take a bag of jewels, too.'

The next day, Sang went into the forest.
Soon, he heard the sound of a flute!

A boy was playing a bamboo flute.
People and animals sat in a circle around the boy.
As the boy played the flute, the bird sang a beautiful song.

Sang walked up to the boy and held up the bag of jewels.

He said, 'I will give you these jewels.
Will you give me that golden bird?'

The boy took the bag of jewels. Then he played his flute.

At once, the bird flew down from the tree
and sat on the boy's shoulder.

He picked up the bird gently, and gave it to Sang.

Sang tied a piece of string round the golden bird's neck, and set off back to the palace.

'That was easy!' he laughed.
'I will give the golden bird to my father –
and he will give me the silver sword!'

But then he heard the flute again.
The golden bird heard it, too.
In a flash of gold, it broke the piece of string –
and flew away into the forest.

Chapter 8

Three foolish sons

The Emperor sent for his three sons.

He said, 'Today is a happy day.
Today the golden bird will be mine!
Now, which of my sons caught it for me?
Jing! Was it you?'

'No, Father,' said Jing. 'I put the bird under my arm –
but when it heard the boy playing the flute, it flew away!'

'Foolish boy!' shouted the Emperor.
'Lin! Did you catch the golden bird?'

'No, Father,' said Lin.
'I put the bird in my basket –
but when it heard the boy playing the flute,
it flew away!'

'Foolish boy!' shouted the Emperor.
'I have **two** foolish sons!
My little Sang!
My youngest son!
Did you catch the golden bird?'

Sang looked into his Father's eyes,
and said, 'No, Father.
I tied the bird on a piece of string – but …'

'I know!' said the Emperor.
'When it heard the boy playing the flute, it flew away!
I have **three** foolish sons.
Not one of them can catch the golden bird –
so **I** must go and catch it myself!'

Chapter 9
The Emperor in danger

All day, the Emperor walked in the forest, but he didn't find the golden bird.

And then, in the evening, he heard a sound. It was the sound of a flute!

The Emperor followed the sound.

After a while, he saw a boy playing a bamboo flute.

'It's Chang!' thought the Emperor.

People and animals sat in a circle around the boy.

And at the top of a tree, the golden bird sat on a branch.
As Chang played the flute, the bird sang a beautiful song.

'It's the golden bird!' thought the Emperor.

Suddenly, the golden bird flew up into the sky.
It sang one short song – and flew away into the forest.

Some wolves were listening to the flute and the bird.
When they saw the Emperor,
they made a circle round him.
They snarled and showed their big, sharp teeth.

'Help me, Chang!' the Emperor shouted
'I am the Emperor and I am in danger!'

'You are the Emperor,' said Chang,
'but you are a greedy, jealous man.
I will help you – but there is a price.
You must give half of your money to your people!'

'Half of my money! But …'

One of the wolves snarled again,
and showed his big, sharp teeth.

'All right, I will do as you say!
Now help me!' the Emperor said.

Chang played the magic flute.
All the wolves went into the forest.

Chapter 10
The party

The Emperor kept his promise.
He went back to the palace,
and he put half of his bags of gold on the ground.

Then he called his three sons.

'Jing! Lin! Sang! I want you to give this gold
to the people!' he said.

That night, the people had a party outside the palace.
Everyone was there – the Emperor, Jing, Lin, Sang,
the old man, Chang and all the animals –
and the Emperor's twenty sheep!

'Three cheers for Chang!' cried the people.
'Three cheers for Chang and his magic flute!'

Chang took out his three bags of jewels.

'We shared the gold,' he said. 'Let's share the jewels, too!'

And high in the night sky, above the palace,
flew a golden bird. It looked down on them all,
and sang its beautiful song.

The Fairy Flute

My brother has a little flute
Of gold and ivory,
He found it on a summer night
Within a hollow tree,
He plays it every morning
And every afternoon,
And all the little singing-birds
Listen to the tune.
He plays it in the meadows,
And everywhere he walks
The flowers start a-nodding
And dancing on their stalks.
He plays it in the village,
And all along the street
The people stop to listen,
The music is so sweet.
And none but he can play it
And none can understand,
Because it is a fairy flute
And comes from Fairyland.

Rose Fyleman

Chinese musical instruments

In the story, Chang played a bamboo flute called a *dizi*. The Chinese still play this instrument today.

There are eight groups of traditional Chinese musical instruments – bamboo, stone, metal, skin, wood, silk, gourd and clay. Here are some of them.

Bamboo instruments

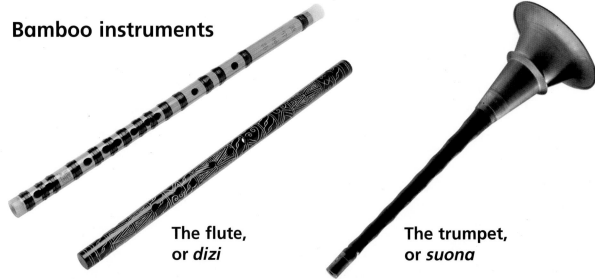

The flute, or *dizi*

The trumpet, or *suona*

Stone instruments

In this instrument, stones of different sizes hang from a frame. The player strikes them with a little hammer.

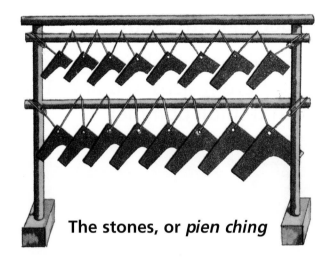

The stones, or *pien ching*

Metal instruments

The gong, or *luo*

The cymbals, or *bo*

The bells, or *bianzhong*

Skin instruments

You can stretch an animal skin over a frame to make a drum. You then strike the skin with a drumstick.

The drum, or *bangu*

Wooden instruments

To make a xylophone, you fix some wooden blocks of different sizes in a line. Then you strike them with a small hammer.

The Chinese xylophone

Silk instruments

These are instruments with strings.
You can use a bow to play some of them.
You pluck the others with your fingers.

The *er-hu*

The *guzheng*

Gourd instruments

You make this instrument from a vegetable called a gourd. It contains bamboo pipes. You blow these to make different notes.

The mouth organ, or *sheng*

Clay instruments

This egg-shaped instrument has got six holes. You close the holes with the ends of your fingers. When you blow the ocarina, each hole makes a different sound.

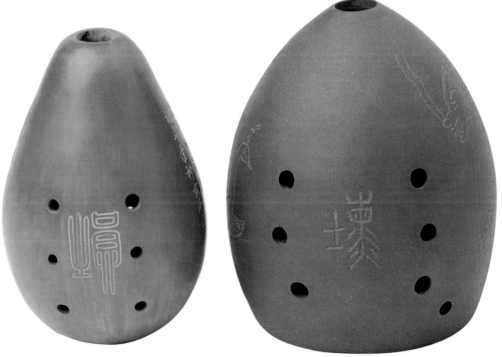

The ocarina, or *xun*

Macmillan Education
Between Towns Road, Oxford OX4 3PP
A division of Macmillan Publishers Limited
Companies and representatives throughout the world

ISBN 1-4050-6010-7
ISBN-13: 978-1-4050-6010-3

First published 2006

Design and layout by Anthony Godber
Illustrated by Peter Simpson
Cover design by Linda Reed & Associates
Cover illustration by Peter Simpson

The authors and publishers would like to thank the following for
permission to reproduce photographs their photographic material:
Alamy pp45(t); Cadmium pp45(mr, mrt), 47(b); Corbis pp44(t, bl, br), 45(r), 46(t);
DK Images pp46(br, bl), 47(t); Getty / Bridgeman pp45(b).

The Series Editor and the Author would like to give
special thanks to Gill McLean for her contribution
in setting up the *Macmillan Explorers* series, for her
continuous encouragement, and for her positive and
practical help and advice throughout its production.

The authors and Publishers are grateful for permission to reprint
the following:
Rose Fyleman 'The Fairy Flute' copyright © Rose Fyleman 1956
from Come Follow Me: Poems for the Young (Evans, 1956),
reprinted by permission of The Society of Authors as the
Literary Representatives of the Estate of Rose Fyleman.

Printed and bound in Egypt by Zamzam Presses

2010 2009 2008 2007 2006
10 9 8 7 6 5 4 3 2 1